For Annie, Eva, Dan, and Dixie
~D. B.

For Aaron and Isaac
~P. I.

Backpack Books
122 Fifth Avenue, New York, NY 10011
ISBN 978-0-7607-8025-1
Printed and bound in Malaysia by Imago
08 09 10 [Imago] 10 9 8 7 6 5 4 3
Library of Congress Cataloging-in-Publication Data
available upon request.
First published in Great Britain 2001 by Little Tiger Press,
an imprint of Magi Publications, London.
David Bedford and Penny Ives have asserted their rights
to be identified as the author and illustrator of this work
under the Copyright, Designs and Patents Act, 1988.

THE LONG JOURNEY HOME

by David Bedford   *Pictures by* Penny Ives

BACKPACKBOOKS

•

NEW YORK

Dixie woke up. What was that noise?
There was something crying, *meow, meow* . . .

so he crept through the hole
in the fence to see who it was.

Behind the fence he found a kitten.
"I've lost my mommy!" it wailed.

Dixie looked around and about. "Does she
have a stripy tail?"
"Yes!" said the kitten. "And pointy ears."
"Follow me," said Dixie. "I'll take you to her."

"Thank you, Dixie!" said the
kitten's mom, but Dixie didn't
hear her because . . .

he'd already gone to see who was hopping
up and down among the long grasses.
Boing! Boing! Boing! it went.

"Why are you bouncing?" asked Dixie.
"I can't fly yet," said the baby owl. "And I'm looking for my mommy."

Boing!

Boing!

Boing!

"Does she live in the trees?"
asked Dixie.
"Yes, she does," said
the baby owl.
"Then follow me,"
Dixie said.

Boing!

Boing!

Boing!

"Thank you, Dixie!" called the owl's mom, but Dixie didn't hear. He'd already gone farther into the woods to see who was making that terrible noise.

YOW-WOW-WOW-WOWWWWWWWWWWWwwwwww

"YOW!" cried the fox cub. "I can't find
my way home."
"Where do you live?" asked Dixie.
"In the side of a hill," said the fox cub.
"Follow me," said Dixie. "I can see
your mommy looking for you."

"Thank you, Dixie," said the fox cub's mom. "But shouldn't you be home by now? It'll soon be dark." Dixie turned to go, but . . .

which way was home?

Everything looked
different in the dark.

Dixie was lost.

"Don't worry," said the foxes,
"we'll show you where to go."
They led Dixie to the edge of
the wood.

"We don't know the way from
here," said the cubs' mom.
Dixie didn't know the way, either.
What was he going to do next?

"Look, Dixie, I can fly now!" called
the baby owl. "Follow us!"
Dixie followed the little owl and his
family through the moonlight until
he came to the long grass.

"We don't know where
to go from here," said the
baby owl.

"But we do," squeaked a small voice. "Come with us."

Dixie followed the kitten and his mom through the tunnels in the grass until . . .

he knew exactly where he was! There was
the hole in the fence, and there, on the
other side, someone was waiting for him.

"I've been looking for you everywhere!" said Dixie's mom. "You shouldn't have gone out on your own in the dark. You could have got lost."